A Fishing I Will Go!

To Charlie,

Good luck in finding your "Reel Adventure!"

Written & Illustrated by:

LISA FRENCH

Lisa French

Palmetto Publishing Group, LLC
www.PalmettoPublishingGroup.com

A Fishing I Will Go!
Copyright ©2017 by Lisa French

All rights reserved. No part of this publication may be reproduced, distributed, stored in a retrieval system, or transmitted, in any form or by any means, including electronic, mechanical, photocopying, recording or otherwise, without the prior written permission of the publisher, except in the case of brief quotations embodied in critical reviews, and certain other non-commercial uses permitted by copyright law.

ISBN-13: 978-1-944313-94-4
ISBN-10: 1-944313-94-X

With love to Michael, Frankie, Leanne, and Kristin.
To my grandchildren, Haley and Ryder.

This book is dedicated to my beloved Mom,
Joyce French, who passed away on February 13, 2017,
and who suffered from chronic progressive multiple
sclerosis. I love and miss you, Mom!

As I cast and I cast
and I CAST, CAST, CAST!

Hi, Mr. Fluke that I caught off the pier.
How can I keep you when you're too small, I hear?

So I throw him back with a
SPLASH, SPLASH, SPLASH!

As I cast and I cast
and I CAST, CAST, CAST!

Hi, Mr. Sea Robin who I cannot fry.
How can I keep you with that croaking cry?

So I throw him back with a
SPLASH, SPLASH, SPLASH!

As I cast and I cast
and I CAST, CAST, CAST!

Hi, Mr. Bluefish with your shiny, silky skin.
How can I keep you with that unhappy grin?

So I throw him back with a
SPLASH, SPLASH, SPLASH!

As I cast and I cast
and I CAST, CAST, CAST!

Hi, Mr. Crab who is caught on my hook.
How can I keep you when you're not the type to cook?

So I throw him back with a
SPLASH, SPLASH, SPLASH!

As I cast and I cast
and I CAST, CAST, CAST!

Hi, Mr. Squid with your tentacles a-stretch.
How can I keep you when you're not a good catch?

So I throw him back with a
SPLASH, SPLASH, SPLASH!

As I cast and I cast
and I CAST, CAST, CAST!

Hi, Mr. Eel, you're a wiggly, slimy sight.
How can I keep you when you put up such a fight?

So I throw him back with a
SPLASH, SPLASH, SPLASH!

As I cast and I cast
and I CAST, CAST, CAST!

Hi, Mr. Blackfish with those human-looking teeth.
How can I keep you when you feast on the reef?

So I throw him back with a
SPLASH, SPLASH, SPLASH!

As I cast and I cast
and I CAST, CAST, CAST!

Hi, Mr. Bass, who swallowed all my bait.
How can I keep you when you're not enough weight?

So I throw him back with a
SPLASH, SPLASH, SPLASH!

As I cast and I cast and I CAST, CAST, CAST!

Hi, Mr. Tuna!!!
You are so big, and you are so tasty.
Throw you back? Now let's not be hasty!

So in my bucket you will go.
I'm running home with you in tow!

Why, you'll look so great
upon my plate!

Add some broccoli and some rice,
and don't forget to add some spice!

I had so much fun, and I love to fish.
The tuna I caught will make a great dish!

About the Author

Lisa French is a proud mother of three beautiful children and two beautiful grandchildren. Although taking care of her mother, who suffered from chronic progressive multiple sclerosis for over 25 years, and raising three children alone, Lisa has survived while having multiple sclerosis herself. She is a fighter!

Lisa has loved to write and draw since she was a child. She also loves to go fishing on Michael's boat, "Reel Adventure." This was the inspiration for *A Fishing I Will Go!*, which is her first published book.

67050181R00017

Made in the USA
Lexington, KY
01 September 2017